A LEGEND
FROM CRAZY HORSE CLAN

by Moses Nelson Big Crow
(Eyo Hiktepi)

Edited by Renée Sansom-Flood

Cover Artist and Illustrations by
Daniel Long Soldier, Oglala Sioux

Tipi Press

P.O. Box 89, Chamberlain, South Dakota 57325

Tipi Press
St. Joseph's Indian School
Chamberlain, South Dakota 57326

Copyright © 1987, 1991, 1996, 2002 by Tipi Press, St. Joseph's
Indian School

Cover art and illustrations by Daniel Long Soldier.
Cover art and story illustrations © Tipi Press, St. Joseph's Indian
School, Chamberlain, South Dakota.
First Edition, Fourth Printing
All Right Reserved

ISBN 1-877976-03-2

Printed by Tipi Press Printing, St. Joseph's Indian School,
Chamberlain, South Dakota.

EDITOR'S NOTE

When he was a child, Moses Nelson Big Crow spent many winter evenings listening to his grandfather tell stories of Lakota life before and after the coming of the white man. As the pampered Hokshi-tokapa, (oldest grandson of the oldest son) Moses regularly got to sleep between Grandma and Grandpa Big Crow in their big iron bed. It was warm, comfortable, and secure to drift off to sleep while grandma sang a lullaby or "gramps" told a story. In the summertime, they all slept outside. Grandma spread blankets and quilts, while gramps brought out his buffalo robe coat. Moses got to sleep on that. At night, under the stars, Moses heard special stories reserved for the Hokshi-tokapa.

A LEGEND FROM CRAZY HORSE CLAN is a story for children of all ages. The historian or student of Indian ways will enjoy the book as much as the child of seven, in whose imagination the baby raccoon Mesu embodies all that is faithful and loving in a small furry pet. Listen carefully to the words of Tashia. The symbolic role of man and of woman is evident throughout the legend. Although the story essentially describes the life of a girl, the narrator is male. Clearly, the legend describes the male viewpoint of manhood, religion, courtship, aging and death. The characters are gentle, yet there is a strong underlying theme of tribal identity. Without a doubt, we are looking at life through the eyes of a warrior.

Moses Big Crow was born February 17, 1937, the first grandchild of Casey Red Shirt, an Oglala, and Henry Big Crow, a Rosebud Sioux. His early years were spent at Upper Cut Meat on the Rosebud Reservation in South Dakota. Before he started school, Moses was free to come and go as he pleased among his many relatives. The tiyospaye, or Lakota extended family, can mean as many as three hundred people, most of whom claim relationship with one another. In the old days of the Sioux, and on some reservations today, cousins are regarded more like brothers, aunts as mothers and uncles as fathers. Moses was part of one large protective shield--his tiyospaye. When he was born, Crazy Horse had been dead only sixty years.

Though much has changed in the life of the Lakota, traditional stories and songs are still passed down from generation to generation. Many are humorous, some teach lessons, and others are told to remind the listener of a tribal leader or event which should not be forgotten.

Indian oral narration is spoken American literature in its finest form. When Lakota children of the 1980s become grandparents themselves, they will tell the legends again. Thanks to Moses Big Crow, one of those legends may well be a A LEGEND FROM CRAZY HORSE CLAN.

Renée Sansom Flood

AUTHOR'S NOTE

I was a boy when my grandfather, Henry Big Crow, told me this Lakóta legend. But now I have no grandchildren to pass it on to.

My grandfather left me this memory so that I would always remember to honor my tiyospaye relatives, Ċunku (Coming Back Angry), Tašunke Witko (Crazy Horse), and Zuya Mani (Goes To War).

There are other Aške Ki Gluwipi (The Ones Who Wrap Their Braids) warriors to honor. Someday, I will tell you another story.

Moses Nelson Big Crow
(Eyo Hiktepi)
March 29, 1987

ACKNOWLEDGEMENTS

I am a full-blood Lakóta. It is hard for me to communicate with non-Indians. It is even harder to translate Lakóta into English and then write what I want to say. The following friends and relatives encouraged me, taught me, and gave me strength to write this memory. I give thanks to them and to WankanTanka, the Great Spirit.

Henry Big Crow

Albert White Hat Sr.

P. R. Gregg

Joe American Horse

Marjorie Haigh

Jack Kreitzer

John McNeill

Cheryl Halsey

Dean Vik

Judy Kuckleburg

Jeff Beringer

Lynne DeLano

Robert W. Dooley

Abbott Denis Quinkert OSB

Reverend Walter and Mrs. Rasmussen

Brother Placid Hellmann OSB

Elliott J. Halsey

Renée Sansom-Flood

Daniel Long Soldier - Artist

Father Tom Westhoven, SCJ

A Legend From Crazy Horse Clan

by Moses Nelson Big Crow

(Eyo Hiktepi)

The baby raccoon sputtered, growled, and kicked against the heavy buffalo robe.

A little Indian girl coo-ed, "Ssshhh, Ena nanik o′ktay k′shto." (Be quiet. Mother will hear you.) "If you don't be quiet, you will be soup," she whispered.

The small creature settled quietly as soft arms encircled him. The young girl sang, "Ah-boo, ah-boo," (Sleep, sleep) until she went back to sleep herself.

Hours earlier far to the south, a great herd of buffalo bedded down for the night. An alert lookout stood guard nearby on a hill. To the west, a thundering lightning storm suddenly changed course and headed east toward the herd. With the sudden appearance of lightning, the entire herd came awake with surprise. In panic, they bolted and stampeded north. In their path was the camp of the legendary War Leader, Chunku (Coming Back Angry). The fearless Warrior Society Chieftain and a group of his clan

The midnight buffalo stampede caught the sleeping village by surprise! The camp was in confusion and panic as men, women and children hurriedly packed anything within reach.

were hunting buffalo. They camped close to a ble chikala (small lake). The men of Chunku Clan hunted buffalo for meat and robes. Soon, they would meet with other Lakota (allies) for spring ceremonies.

The midnight buffalo stampede caught the sleeping village by surprise! The camp was in confusion and panic as men, women, and children hurriedly packed anything within reach. They knew the terrible destruction of stampeding buffalo. Many belongings were left behind...bags of arrow points, captured Army blankets, and buffalo robes. Accidentally left behind under a buffalo robe was the little girl named Tashia Gnupa (Meadowlark) and her baby raccoon Mesu (Little Brother).

In the morning, the sun rose high with bright sunshine. All was eerily quiet on the flat, open prairie. The air smelled of dust and manure and silent were the throats of the meadowlarks. There on the ground lay a buffalo robe with a small lump in the middle. The lump moved, then bucked. Carrying a baby raccoon, an Indian wichinchala (girl) in deerskin dress crawled out from under the heavy robe.

The girl called out, "Ena, Ena, wanna wake-ta k´shto. Mesu mni che kay k´shto." (Mother, mother, I am awake now. Mesu says he wants water.)

The girl rubbed her eyes awake, surprised to find herself alone. Her mother and father and brothers were gone. There were no horses or people. There was nothing. She went to sleep in the middle of a noisy village with children, horses and

Tashia and her baby raccoon waited many days by their buffalo robe, but no one found them.

Daniel Long Solder
87

barking dogs. Now, there was nothing at all but an awful smell in the air and a cloud of dust.

Tashia and her baby raccoon waited many days by their buffalo robe, but no one found them. They drank lake water and ate whatever they found among the bushes and weeds on the prairie. As summer wore on, the lake grew lively with birds and animals. Tashia tried to build a fire, but she could never make the rocks work for her. Still, she managed to find enough to eat. Mesu got bigger and sassier every day. They sat and chatted with the meadowlarks and learned many things. The little birds gossiped and sang songs to make happy the hearts of the two stranded friends. Tashia spoke often with the birds for which she was named. Her parents and brothers thought she chattered like a bird, but they loved her dearly. Mesu, the raccoon, had been their gift to her. Before the raccoon she had a magpie, but one day it flew too close to somebody's dog.

Many were the times Tashia sat in the shade of the lakeside willows crying silently for her mother, father and brothers. Poor Mesu licked her tears. He tried everything he could think of to comfort his beautiful friend. He even tried to wash her hands, like he washed the things he ate. Pretty soon, he had Tashia laughing so hard she forgot her troubles. This made him feel very important.

One day, the two friends decided to spend an afternoon around a little cedar tree on a hill. Mesu was extra happy because he knew that many fat gnugnushka (grasshoppers)

Tashia dragged the buffalo robe to the tree and they crawled under it and fell asleep. While they slept, a buffalo herd ranged close to the lake.

lived near the tree. He wanted Tashia to eat some nice big ones. He did not like to see his friend with hollow cheeks and big eyes. After their snack, Tashia dragged the buffalo robe to the tree and they crawled under it and fell asleep. While they slept, a buffalo herd ranged close to the lake.

Nearby, a young buffalo calf bleated bark-like sounds. He explored the new world around him, challenging everything in sight. After all, he was a bull. Looking around, he saw another calf sleeping in the shade of a cedar tree on a hill. He decided to attack to show strength and manliness. Head down, the young bull charged. Suddenly, he stopped! There under the tree was a strange looking animal. The calf went over and sniffed it. Then, he bleated a few friendly (but manly) bellows. Nothing happened. Next, he tried to lick the animal, like his mother licked him. The smell and taste were strange. The fur he was licking gave way to something smooth and salty. But that was alright, so he gave a few bleats of approval.

Mesu was awakened by slurping sounds. A heavy push knocked the wind out of him. Instantly, he was on his hind legs standing upright, staring up into the big, black eyes of a buffalo standing over him! Mesu did not need another look. He turned in panic and ran smack into the little cedar tree! He was knocked dizzy and flat on his back. Hurt and full of terror, he leaped to his feet and made his second escape. Running at top speed, Mesu remembered he had left his friend Tashia at the mercy of that giant beast.

When Tashia sat up, she was forehead to forehead with the buffalo! Each of them was shocked to see the other.

Meanwhile, the baby buffalo blinked his eyes and gazed in wonder at the crazy creature that ran out of the buffalo hide with a screech. Then, it tried to knock down that little tree! He watched as it ran around in a circle and headed straight toward him.

The calf's wet, rough tongue woke Tashia. The buffalo snorted and sniffed her hair. She arched her back and sneezed twice. When Tashia sat up, she was forehead to forehead with the buffalo! Each of them was shocked to see the other. Mesu came to a stop a few feet from them and began nervously washing himself all over. He did not take his eyes off his Tashia and the buffalo.

Moving very slowly, Tashia-Gnupa rose on her hands and feet. She breathed slowly and quietly. She remembered that her father taught her brothers all the tactics of caution. They had to stay alert to observe and attack from the best advantage. Now, her memory was backtracking like a runaway horse. She saw Mesu coming in closer, but she knew a raccoon was no match for a buffalo. Even a young buffalo with floppy ears, clumsy hooves, and knobby joints was dangerous. A buffalo is a buffalo.

Tashia spoke quietly to Mesu and braced herself. Mesu was ready. Suddenly, Tashia tore away and ran as fast as her feet ever moved. Mesu hid behind the tree. The baby Buffalo stood there puzzled. Then, he realized he had made a friend who wanted to play. With a loud bleat he jumped up, spun around, and ran after Tashia who was headed downhill.

The calf raced beside his new friend, who ran like the wind. Tashia and the calf were looking at each other and did not see the dry gully ahead. They left the ground together and landed head-first in the dirt.

Mesu, seeing this, took after the buffalo to save Tashia. Despite Tashia's headstart, it did not take long for the calf to catch her. He looked happily at the girl and bleated out, "Hello!"

The calf raced beside his new friend, who ran like the wind. Tashia and the calf were looking at each other and did not see the dry gully ahead. They left the ground together and landed head-first in the dirt. Mesu showed up full of rage. He wanted to settle this buffalo business once and for all. The calf was sitting on the ground. Mesu never saw a buffalo sit before. He wondered why he could not sit like that. Why did he always have to run side-ways, even in emergencies?

Meanwhile, the mother buffalo looked for her calf. She bellowed an alarm. The herd became a hunting party as every cow and bull looked for the stray calf. The herd sensed danger and began to round up calves. The bulls formed a circle to defend the cows.

Tashia was busy trying to get rid of the calf. She tried to scream at it to go away, but the calf thought she was just playing. Mesu ran straight up to him and looked him in the eye. The girl finally gave up and went down to the lake for a drink of water and something to eat. The buffalo followed her. He watched as she took a long hearty drink from the lake. There by the edge, she ate Ponkee (potatoes) and wild onions. Then, she stopped at a berry patch for some sweets and a rest. Tashia wondered what her brothers were eating and where. She wished she could see them again. All she

Next morning, Tashia got up at dawn to pray. She had been taught to pray in this manner since she could remember. Mesu stood beside her while she gave thanks to Wakan-Tanka (The Great Spirit) for letting her live to greet the sun for another day.

had was Mesu, their gift to her. Now too, she had a funny buffalo calf that would not leave her side.

The roaring mother cow spotted her lost calf and the two-legged creature. The cow lowered her horns as she charged the little man-person. The buffalo calf barreled in front of Tashia to defend his friend. He was not going to lose his new friend and that was all there was to it! After much disagreement, the cow finally agreed to her calf's wishes. She ignored the man-creature and that other disgusting, furry thing that followed.

Next morning, Tashia got up at dawn to pray. She had been taught to pray in this manner since she could remember. Mesu stood beside her while she gave thanks to WakanTanka (The Great Spirit) for letting her live to greet the sun for another day. After her prayers, the bull calf taught Tashia how to nurse from the mother cow. Tashia gave Mesu some milk in the palm of her hand and he thought a little more would not hurt at all. Then, all three friends sat in the shade of a tree gazing at the beauty of the lake and prairie.

Tashia turned to look at her buffalo friend. He was sleepy. "What if you were a handsome warrior?" she said to the drowsy calf. "You would bring my father, Chunku, many fine horses, beads for my mother, and real steel knives for my brothers. You would take me away to be your wife. I would have children, cook your food, sew your bags, and bead your moccasins. I would hunt for your arrowhead stones and be your sweet wife and love you very much." The calf

One afternoon, a lookout brought news of an approaching rider. The buffalo always bellowed twice to alert one another of a horse and rider.

yawned, sniffed and shook his floppy ears as a fly buzzed him too close. "I would call you my Wechokcha (husband) and make you happy, wouldn't I?" she asked. The calf opened his mouth wide and yawned again. "Then, it is settled. You are my Wechokcha. From now on, I will be your wife." The newlywed calf went to sleep, Mesu hunted fat grasshoppers and Tashia hummed a song. She looked at the lonely hills and thought that she had not been this happy in a long time.

It was the second wi (month) since Tashia and Mesu joined the buffalo herd. One afternoon, a lookout brought news of an approaching rider. The buffalo always bellowed twice to alert one another of a horse and rider. The faithful Wechokcha taught Tashia the buffalo language. She watched as bulls gathered in protective positions. Tashia wondered if it could be someone from her father's camp out looking for her. As the rider came up the creek, Tashia came out of the draw where she had been hiding. She approached the rider with caution. Tashia almost cried when she saw that it was not one of her own people. It was a washichu (whiteman). She remembered her brothers talking about these people who lived many days travel to the rising sun. Why was this one here?

The man's face was covered with strange fur. He wore a buckskin jacket beaded with a Kungi-wichasha (Crow) design. The bag on his belt was also from the Crow nation. Tashia recognized the Oshkay-ki (Wrapped Braids) arrows of

She approached the horse carefully. It jerked nervously as she crept up. Tashia gently cut the strings on the pack behind the saddle. The pack slid off and the horse stood shaking. It turned and sniffed the girl, then neighed in terror and jerked backward as Tashia hung on.

her people sticking out of the man's chest. She knew the Oshkay-ki Warrior Society guarded the land of the Lakota. Her father, Chunku, was their leader.

The man's shunka-wakan (horse) came to the creek to drink. When the horse leaned over to drink, the man slumped forward and fell to the ground. He did not move. Tashia slowly walked up to him. She remembered her father's words, "Anyone or anything you do not know will hurt you. Always be alert." Her father's words raced through her mind as she came closer to the motionless figure. She checked the washichu, but it was too late. "It is a good day to die," she said for him as she looked up at the clear blue sky. Then, she thought of the arrows. This man fought her people. He might even have killed one of her relatives. Tashia bent down and quickly searched him. She took the beautiful knife he carried and the beaded belt and bag. She approached the horse carefully. It jerked nervously as she crept up. Tashia gently cut the strings on the pack behind the saddle. The pack slid off and the horse stood shaking. It turned and sniffed the girl, then neighed in terror and jerked backward as Tashia hung on. Suddenly, the head stall broke and she fell backward into the creek. The horse, now free, ran out of sight.

Mesu joined Tashia-Gnupa as she sat crying over the lost horse. She wanted that horse! In anger, she threw the bridle as far as she could. Then, she went after it. Tashia knew how many things she could make with the leather straps. Meanwhile, Mesu busied himself checking every pocket of the deadman's clothing. Tashia and Mesu took everything

Tashia's people, the Lakota, tried to prevent the whitemen from killing buffalo. But as the washichu came closer and closer, the great buffalo herds grew smaller.

that would be of use to them. Tashia found tools to sew with, blankets, and a container for water and meat. Before she left, Tashia thanked the dead man for the things he had left behind and wished him a happy journey.

So went the years when Tashia-Gnupa lived as a buffalo in a buffalo nation. Although she was taught to avoid men, that part of her that was human always yearned to be with her own people. As the years passed, Tashia's buffalo husband, Wechokcha, grew older and wiser. Mesu, the raccoon, had a different family every year, but he stayed close to his young Lakota friend. Tashia's keen eyesight played an important role in the survival of the herd. She always listened to the little willow birds and the small animals that alert each other to danger. The herd was ready to move if men came near.

Tashia's people, the Lakota, tried to prevent the whitemen from killing buffalo. But as the washichu came closer and closer, the great buffalo herds grew smaller. Always under pressure, Tashia's herd moved north. One day, the herd came to the lake where they first found Tashia and Mesu. The lake was as beautiful as ever. Wechokcha, Mesu and Tashia saw the cedar tree on the hill and they all laughed about their first meeting.

Several days later, while all three were lounging under the tree, a tall Indian suddenly appeared. He carried a monzawakan (iron with unbelievable powers), and he spoke

When the two men came back to check on the girl, they found her by the side of the fallen buffalo. One of the scouts, Ona-Shola (Fast Walker), returned to his people with fresh buffalo meat, while Goes To War remained with the grieving girl. He sat in close vigil all that day and night while Tashia mourned.

words Tashia knew. "Netu-way who wo? Toki-yaton hun, ya-he who wo? (Who are you and where do you come from?) Tashia stood speechless. Many years had passed since she last heard the Lakota language.

While Tashia stood staring, her buffalo husband, Wechokcha, lowered his head to attack. In fury, he charged the akichita (warrior). Out of nowhere, a rider came forward to meet the buffalo in battle. Wechokcha bellowed with happiness as he met the courageous Oshkay-ki head-on. The bull threw his full weight against the horse, flipping the animal over on top of the Indian. He put his massive head to the ground and butted the horse to get at the rider underneath. Just as Wechokcha's horns reached the man, a rifle shot sounded. The great Wechokcha dropped like a rock and lay still.

Tashia ran screaming to her buffalo husband. There she suffered a true broken heart and lost consciousness. Mesu's cry of sorrow could be heard over the prairie.

Zuya-Moni (Goes To War), the Lakota who killed Wechokcha, went to help his friend get out from under the horse. When the two men came back to check on the girl, they found her by the side of the fallen buffalo. One of the scouts, Ona-Shola (Fast Walker), returned to his people with fresh buffalo meat, while Goes To War remained with the grieving girl. He sat in close vigil all that day and night while Tashia mourned.

At dawn, the warrior took sage from his pack, held it in his

For three days Tashia did not speak or drink water. She stood with the warrior in his morning prayer, but she remained in mourning and he respected her silence.

raised hands and prayed to Tunkanshila WakanTanka (Grandfather Great Spirit). He asked that Tunkanshila bring courage to the sorrowful girl. While praying, he felt the presence of the old raccoon who joined him in prayer. The man sang a song and as he sang, he remembered the legend of the lost child of Chunku Clan. Chunku, the great leader of the Oshkay-ki, lost a daughter years before when a buffalo stampede destroyed his village. The child carried a pet raccoon named Mesu. Since that day, the two lost friends became a legend in the clan. As the young warrior watched the girl and her raccoon he wondered to himself, "Could this be Tashia-Gnupa and Mesu?" He knew hunters and scouts who claimed they had seen a girl riding in a buffalo herd. Maybe it was not a girl. Maybe it was nothing at all. There was only one way to find out. The Lakota reached out his hand to the raccoon saying, "Mesu, Mesu, letchiya hu wo!" (Little Brother, Little Brother, come over here.) When the old raccoon heard his name, he glided over sideways and put out his cupped paws for something to eat. The warrior then knew the truth.

For three days Tashia did not speak or drink water. She stood with the warrior in his morning prayer, but she remained in mourning and he respected her silence. On the fourth day, he prepared a meal and she ate with him. Then Tashia went to the little tree on the hill and said, "Woglaka na!" (Talk). It surprised him to hear the girl speak Lakota, but he was glad her silence was over. Goes To War told Tashia he was sorry her buffalo was dead.

Soon, Goes To War led Tashia into camp. Word passed quickly among the people. Everyone was curious, but they were polite and kept a respectful distance from the legendary girl. When Tashia came to the Warrior's Lodge, the people brought gifts to her.

"The bull died bravely. He protected you," he said. "There is no greater honor than to meet a strong enemy in death."

At this she answered, "You will take me with you and I will be your wife. I will cook your meals, have children for you, sew your moccasins and find arrow stones and beads on the ant hills. I can make you very happy. You will be my Wechokcha forever. All this is so because you killed my husband who loved me very much. He fought and killed anyone who tried to hurt me, but you killed him and Mesu saw everything, didn't you Mesu?" The raccoon glided up, stood straight up on his hind legs and vouched for everything she said.

Goes To War was puzzled. The young woman spoke like a five year-old child. He remembered she had been lost when just a small girl and had never spoken Lakota since. The warrior told Tashia he would take her to his camp only three days ride into the hills. There she would find her mother waiting anxiously for her long lost daughter.

Towards evening of the second day, they came to the foothills. Looking down a wide valley, they saw the smoke from many cooking fires. As they rode, Goes To War told Tashia of her father Chunku and his fight with the Crow nation. Tashia's two brothers were killed in battle by Crow warriors and her father vowed to fight the Crow nation forever.

Soon, Goes To War led Tashia into camp. Word passed

Outside the lodge, men had a drum going. The old people sang welcome songs to the girl who returned from the dead. They rejoiced when the lost child reunited with her mother.

quickly among the people. Everyone was curious, but they were polite and kept a respectful distance from the legendary girl. When Tashia came to the Warrior's Lodge, the people brought gifts to her. Each person accepted her as a niece, cousin or granddaughter.

Outside the lodge, men had a drum going. The old people sang welcome songs to the girl who returned from the dead. They rejoiced when the lost child reunited with her mother. From that day on, the clan sang songs and told legends of the human child who lived with a buffalo nation.

In the years that passed, Tashia married an Oshkay-ki warrior. Their life together was long and happy. By the time they grew old one of their sons was the pride of all Lakota. He led his Oshkay-ki brothers into battle against the United States Army and was known as Tashunke Witko (Crazy Horse). Remember takoja (grandchild) that I have told you this.

Tashia Gnupa mia yelo.
(I am the meadowlark.)

Tashia Gnupa mia yelo.*
(I am the meadowlark.)

*Tashia Gnupa is a Siouan Onomatopoeia.
The words sound like the song of the meadowlark.

In the years that passed, Tashia
married an Oshkay-ki warrior. Their
life together was long and happy.

LAKOTA WORD GLOSSARY

PRONUNCIATION	LAKOTA SPELLING	ENGLISH
Ena nanik ó ktay kʹshto.	Ina nanihʹun kte ksto.	Mother will hear you.
Ah-boo	Ah-boo	a lullaby or croon to sleep.
Chunku	Cunzek-ku or cunzeka-ku	Coming Back Angry
ble chikala	ble cikʹala	small lake
Lakota	Lakota	Allies
Tashia Gnupa	Tasiya gmuka	Meadowlark
Mesu	Misun or Misunkala	Little Brother
wichinchala	wicincala	girl
Wanna wake-ta kʹshto.	Wana wekta ksto.	I am awake now.
Mesu mni che kay kʹshto.	Misun mni cin keyeksto.	Mesu says he wants water.
gnugnushka	gnugnuska	grasshopper
ponkee	pon kua or blo	potato
wechokcha	wica hca	husband
wi	wi	month
washichu	wasicu	whiteman
Kungi-wichasha	Kangi wicasa	Crow Indian
Oshkay-ki	Aske-ki or Aske Gluwipi	The Ones Who Have Wrapped Braids
shunka-wakan	sunka wakan	horse
monza-wakan	maza wakan	Iron with unbelievable powers

Netu-way who wo?	Nituwe huwo?	Who are you?
Toki-yaton hun ya-he who wo?	Tokiya tanhan yahi huwo?	Where do you come from?
akichita	akicita	warrior or soldier
Zuya-Moni	Zuya Mani	Goes to War
Ona-Shola	Ona S'ola	Fast Walker
Tunkanshila	Tunkansila	grandfather
WakanTanka	WakanTanka	Great Spirit
Letchiya hu wo!	Leciya u wo!	Come over here!
Woglaka na!	Woglaka na!	Talk!
takoja	takoja	grandchild
Tashia Gnupa mia yelo	Tasiya Gmuka miye yelo.	I am the Meadowlark.
Tashunke Witko	Tasunke Witko	Crazy Horse
Tiyoshpiay	Tiyospaye	Extended Family